ROBIN HOOD

OUTLAW OF SHERWOOD FOREST

AN ENGLISH LEGEND

STORY BY
PAUL D. STORRIE

PENCILS AND INKS BY
THOMAS YEATES

IRELAND

ROBIN HOOD
OUTLAW OF SHERWOOD FOREST

AN
ENGLISH
LEGEND

IRISH SEA

NOTTINGHAMSHIRE
(HOME OF SHERWOOD FOREST)

•NOTTINGHAM

ENGLAND

LERNER BOOKS LONDON • NEW YORK • MINNEAPOLIS

Robin Hood may or may not have been an actual person. Real or not, his adventures have delighted readers, listeners and viewers for centuries. To write this particular book, author Paul D. Storrie relied heavily on the earliest versions of the Robin Hood stories available: the lyrics to the medieval songs about Robin and his followers. His research also included the excellent books Robin Hood by J. C. Holt and Robin Hood: A Complete Study of the English Outlaw by Stephen Thomas Knight. Artist Thomas Yeates referred to books by great illustrators of the past, including Howard Pyle, Harold Foster, and N. C. Wyeth.

STORY BY PAUL D. STORRIE

PENCILS AND INKS BY THOMAS YEATES
WITH TOD SMITH AND KEN HOOPER

COLOURING BY HI-FI DESIGN

LETTERING BY BILL HAUSER

CONSULTANT: ANDREW SCHEIL
ASSISTANT PROFESSOR OF ENGLISH,
UNIVERSITY OF MINNESOTA

Graphic Universe™ is a trademark of Lerner Publishing Group, Inc.

First published in the United Kingdom in 2010 by
Lerner Books,
Dalton House,
60 Windsor Avenue,
London SW19 2RR

Website address: www.lernerbooks.co.uk

This edition edited for UK publication in 2010.

British Library Cataloguing in Publication Data

Storrie, Paul D.
    Robin Hood : outlaw of Sherwood Forest.
    1. Robin Hood (Legendary character)—Comic books, strips, etc.—Juvenile literature. I. Title
    398.2'2-dc22

ISBN-13: 978 0 7613 5395 9

Printed in China

TABLE OF CONTENTS

HOW ROBIN CAME TO SHERWOOD

*N*OW LISTEN CLOSELY, GENTLE FRIENDS, ALL THOSE WHOSE HEARTS ARE GOOD; AND YOU SHALL HEAR OF A BRAVE YEOMAN, HIS NAME WAS ROBIN HOOD.

LONG AGO, IN THE KINGDOM OF ENGLAND, THERE LIVED A MAN NAMED ROBIN HOOD, THE GREATEST ARCHER THAT EVER LIVED. ALTHOUGH HE WAS AN OUTLAW, HE ONLY ROBBED THOSE WHO WERE CRUEL TO POOR AND HONEST FOLK.

BUT BEFORE HE WAS AN OUTLAW, HE WAS JUST A YOUNG MAN WITH HIGH HOPES FOR THE FUTURE. THOSE HOPES LED HIM, ONE BRIGHT MAY MORNING, TO LEAVE HIS HOME IN THE VILLAGE OF LOCKSLEY AND CUT THROUGH SHERWOOD FOREST ON HIS WAY TO THE TOWN OF NOTTINGHAM.

A CHEAT, A COWARD, AND A BAD ARCHER!

STILL, EVEN A BAD ARCHER CAN MAKE A LUCKY SHOT!

EVEN THOUGH HIS SHOTS FELL SHORT, THE FORESTERS KNEW THAT ROBIN COULD HIT ANY OF THEM AS EASILY AS HE HAD THE DEER. THEY SCRAMBLED TO HIDE BEFORE HE CHANGED HIS MIND AND TOOK BETTER AIM.

THAT SHOULD GIVE THEM PAUSE. TIME I WAS AWAY.

NOW YOU'VE DONE IT, ROBIN HOOD. AS IF KILLING ONE OF THE KING'S DEER WASN'T ENOUGH, YOU'VE FIRED ON THE KING'S FORESTERS.

YOU'RE OUTLAWED FOR CERTAIN.

NO GOING HOME NOW. IT'S LIFE IN SHERWOOD FOR YOU.

AT LEAST YOU'LL HAVE GOOD COMPANY, THEN!

WHO...?

I'VE BEEN OUTLAWED, ROBIN!

HELLO, ROBIN. HOW LONG HAS IT BEEN?

BUT WHY?

MY SOUL! CAN IT BE MY OLD FRIEND, *MUCH* THE MILLER'S SON? WHAT ARE YOU DOING HERE?

YOU KNOW HOW HARD THINGS HAVE BEEN BACK HOME. BETWEEN THE RENTS AND THE TAXES, THERE'S BEEN LESS GRAIN TO MILL.

WE BARELY HAD ENOUGH TO EAT LAST WINTER.

WHAT COULD I DO? I CREPT DOWN TO SHERWOOD TO GET SOME MEAT FOR MY FAMILY.

DON'T WORRY, ROBIN. WE'LL SHOW YOU HOW TO GET BY IN SHERWOOD.

JUST HAD THE BAD LUCK TO RUN INTO SOME FORESTERS AS I WAS DRAGGING IT BACK HOME! I ONLY BARELY GOT AWAY.

THERE ARE MANY MORE LIKE US, OUTLAWED FOR NO GOOD REASON. WE LOOK OUT FOR ONE ANOTHER.

THIS HERE IS *WILL STUTELY.* HIS STORY IS THE SAME, BUT HIS WIFE AND CHILDREN WERE THE ONES GOING HUNGRY.

LATER ...

WE'RE ALL *GOOD* MEN FORCED INTO THIS LIFE BY UNFAIR LAWS OR THOSE WHO ENFORCE THE LAW AS IT SUITS THEM.

TRUE. BUT THERE'S JUST NOTHING WE CAN *DO* ABOUT IT.

YOU SAID THAT THERE ARE MORE MEN LIKE US, SCATTERED ABOUT THE FOREST, DIDN'T YOU, WILL?

YES, WHAT OF IT?

WHAT IF WE GATHER THEM ALL TOGETHER AND GIVE THEM THREE SUITS OF LINCOLN GREEN AND TWENTY MARKS EACH YEAR IF THEY'LL STAND WITH US?

MAYBE THERE IS! THEY'VE MADE US OUTLAWS, SO LET'S PLAY THE PART.

BUT WHY, ROBIN? AND HOW COULD WE PAY FOR IT ALL?

SIMPLE, MUCH! WE'LL CHARGE EVERY CRUEL NOBLE AND GREEDY CHURCHMAN A HEARTY *TOLL* TO PASS THROUGH *SHERWOOD!*

BUT HONEST YEOMEN, POOR FARMERS, TRADESMEN, AND EVEN GOOD-HEARTED KNIGHTS WILL PASS FOR FREE OR GET WHAT HELP WE CAN GIVE.

AND WE WILL BOTHER NO WOMAN, YOUNG OR OLD, ALONG HER WAY.

THEN EACH OF US MAY SEND SOMETHING HOME TO FAMILY AND FRIENDS TO KEEP THEM FED AND CLOTHED.

ARE YOU WITH ME, MEN?

AYE!!

13

ROBIN HOOD AND LITTLE JOHN

WHY SO GLUM, ROBIN?

AYE, YOUR SCHEME HAS WORKED WONDERS THESE LAST FEW MONTHS.

WE LIVE BETTER THAN WE DID, AND THE MONEY WE SEND HOME IS A BOON TO OUR KIN.

WHY, WE'VE EVEN HELPED POOR STRANGERS THAT CAME OUR WAY! YOU SHOULD BE GLAD!

I AM! IT'S JUST THAT THINGS HAVE BEEN SO *QUIET* LATELY.

IT'S BEEN DAYS SINCE A FAT ABBOT OR LORD HAS STUMBLED INTO OUR LOOKOUTS ALONG SHERWOOD'S PATHS AND ROADS. THEY'RE GETTING CAREFUL, AND I'M GROWING BORED!

MAYBE IT'S TIME I WENT OUT AND LOOKED FOR SOME *ADVENTURE!*

WE'LL COME WITH YOU, ROBIN.

NO NEED. I'LL BE FINE ON MY OWN.

I PROMISE THAT IF I'M IN TROUBLE, I'LL BLOW THREE NOTES ON MY HUNTING HORN. IF YOU HEAR THAT, COME RUNNING!

ROBIN WALKED THROUGH THE FOREST FOR HOURS, CHECKING THE ROADS AND PATHS FOR TRAVELLERS, BUT HE WAS BEGINNING TO THINK HE WAS THE ONLY ONE OUT AND ABOUT ON THAT FINE AUTUMN DAY.

OH HO! IT LOOKS LIKE ONE OF THE TREES HAS DECIDED TO TAKE A STROLL. I'D BEST MOVE QUICKLY IF I WANT TO REACH THE BRIDGE BEFORE HIM!

BUT WHEN THE TALL STRANGER SAW THAT ROBIN MEANT TO CROSS FIRST, HE HURRIED TO THE BRIDGE TOO.

STAND BACK, MY TOWERING FRIEND, SO I MAY CROSS!

HA! IT WOULD TAKE A BETTER MAN THAN *YOU* TO MAKE *ME* STEP ASIDE! YOU CAN CROSS AFTER ME.

ROBIN HOOD AND THE POTTER

THE NEXT SPRING, ROBIN HOOD AND LITTLE JOHN WERE WATCHING WATLING STREET, WAITING FOR SOMEONE WHOSE PURSE WAS TOO HEAVY.

ugh! WE WAKE EARLY TO CATCH SOME KNIGHT OR ABBOT AND GET AN HONEST TRADESMAN INSTEAD!

HONEST, NOTHING. I KNOW THAT POTTER FROM WENTBRIDGE. HE CHARGES TOO MUCH AND LOOKS DOWN ON HONEST FOLK.

IT WOULD SERVE HIM RIGHT TO PAY OUR TOLL. DON'T WORRY, THOUGH. HE'S A COWARD.

THREATEN HIM AND HE'LL PAY UP SOON ENOUGH.

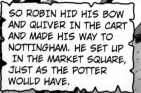

SO ROBIN HID HIS BOW AND QUIVER IN THE CART AND MADE HIS WAY TO NOTTINGHAM. HE SET UP IN THE MARKET SQUARE, JUST AS THE POTTER WOULD HAVE.

THE FINEST POTS IN NOTTINGHAM, THIS IS WHAT I SELL! PLUS THE FINEST PLATES AND BOWLS AND JUGS, ALL OF THESE AS WELL!

I WANT NO FAT CHURCHMEN OR PROUD NOBLEMEN BUYING POTS FROM ME. WHAT SHOULD COST JUST ONE PENNY, I SHALL CHARGE THEM THREE!

FOR THEM ONE PENNY BUYS AS MUCH AS THREE, FOR THEY'RE THE ONES I LIKE BEST, BUYING POTS FROM ME!

EXCEPT, OF COURSE, FOR MAIDENS FAIR. FOR THEM A SPECIAL FEE.

A KISS FROM THEM IS ALL I ASK, TO GET A POT FOR FREE!

I DO NOT CARE IF MERCHANTS BUY, SO NORMAL PRICE THEY GET. BUT HONEST WIVES AND FAIR MAIDS GET THE BEST PRICE YET!

ONE AT A TIME, LADIES! I'VE POTS AND PLATES AND BOWLS AND JUGS FOR ALL.

WHILE ROBIN SOLD HIS WARES, THE SHERIFF OF NOTTINGHAM'S WIFE CAME BY WITH MARIAN FITZWALTER, THE DAUGHTER OF A LOCAL LORD.

IT IS A SHAME, MARIAN, THAT THIS JOLLY POTTER CHARGES EXTRA FOR THE NOBILITY.

I LIKE HIS SPIRIT, BUT NOT HIS PRICE!

TARRY A MOMENT, GOOD LADY, PLEASE!

YOU ARE NOTHING LIKE THE STRUTTING NOBLES THAT I DISLIKE, AND AN HONEST WIFE CAN BE FOUND IN PEASANT'S SHACK OR KNIGHT'S MANOR!

WHAT ABOUT THE SHERIFF'S HALL?

ARE YOU OUR GOOD SHERIFF'S WIFE? FOR THAT ALONE, I WOULD GIVE YOU A SPECIAL PRICE!

IF YOU WILL TELL ME THE NAME OF THE BEAUTIFUL GIRL WITH YOU, I'LL GIVE YOU HALF OF WHAT I HAVE LEFT FOR FREE.

AND IF YOU CAN GET HER TO GIVE ME A KISS, SHE CAN HAVE THE REST!

WHY THAT'S MARIAN, THE DAUGHTER OF LORD FITZWALTER, MY HUSBAND'S FRIEND.

AS FOR THE KISS, THAT WOULD BE UP TO HER.

HOW COULD I REFUSE SUCH AN OFFER?

HMM. NOW HOW WILL WE GET ALL THESE POTS TO MY HOME?

I KNOW! POTTER, IF YOU WILL TAKE THEM BY CART, YOU MAY SHARE OUR SUPPER.

BESIDES, MY HUSBAND HAS BEEN IN A BAD MOOD, WHAT WITH THIS OUTLAW ROBIN HOOD CAUSING SO MUCH TROUBLE. IT WOULD DO HIM GOOD TO MEET SUCH A HAPPY SOUL!

HOW COULD I REFUSE SUCH AN OFFER?

SOON ROBIN FOUND HIMSELF AT THE SHERIFF'S TABLE. BUT SINCE THEY HAD NEVER MET, THE SHERIFF DID NOT GUESS THAT THE HUMBLE POTTER WAS THE INFAMOUS OUTLAW HE LONGED TO CAPTURE.

MY WIFE TELLS ME YOU ARE A CAREFREE SOUL, PRACTICALLY GIVING AWAY YOUR WARES!

WELL, IT JUST SEEMS TO ME THAT WHEN A MAN HAS WHAT HE NEEDS, HE SHOULD BE SATISFIED WITH THAT.

HA! SPOKEN LIKE A MAN WITH SMALL NEEDS!

YOUR WIFE SAYS *YOU* NEED CHEERING UP. SOMETHING ABOUT THIS OUTLAW, ROBIN HOOD?

I BEGIN TO HATE THAT NAME! IT'S ALL I HEAR FROM PEOPLE WHO DON'T HAVE SENSE ENOUGH TO TRAVEL WITH GUARDS WHEN THEY GO THROUGH SHERWOOD!

IF I EVER MEET THIS SCOUNDREL FACE-TO-FACE, I'LL NEVER HAVE TO HEAR HIS NAME AGAIN!

MAYBE I CAN HELP YOU THERE. YOU SEE, I KNOW THIS ROBIN HOOD.

FOR FORTY MARKS, I WILL TAKE YOU TO THE FOREST TOMORROW AND *PROMISE* YOU WILL SEE HIM.

I WOULD GLADLY PAY *TWICE* THAT. BUT TELL ME, HOW IS IT THAT YOU KNOW THIS OUTLAW?

WHY, I GREW UP WITH HIM. HE'S NEVER DONE ME ANY HARM, BUT SEEING HOW MUCH YOU WANT TO MEET HIM, WHAT ELSE CAN I DO?

JUST DON'T TAKE *TOO* MANY SOLDIERS WITH YOU. THE OUTLAWS MIGHT HEAR THEM COMING AND STAY HIDDEN.

HMMM. THAT SEEMS WISE. I WILL TAKE ONLY MY BEST MEN.

OUT OF MY WAY, YOU USELESS FOOL!

LET'S GO OUT TO THE COURTYARD AND HAVE A SHOOTING MATCH! THE BEST ARCHERS WILL GO WITH US IN THE MORNING.

29

INCREDIBLE! AN ARCHER AS GOOD AS YOU SHOULD BE IN MY SERVICE.

I'M FLATTERED, BUT LET'S WAIT UNTIL TOMORROW BEFORE WE SPEAK OF SUCH THINGS.

THE NEXT MORNING, ROBIN, THE SHERIFF, AND HIS MEN SET OUT FOR SHERWOOD FOREST.

QUIET, NOW. THE OUTLAWS ARE NEARBY. DON'T WORRY, THOUGH. I HAVE A WAY TO DRAW THEM OUT.

TIRRAH! TIRRAH!

TIRRAH!

ARE YOU INSANE?

NOW WE'LL NEVER FIND THEM!

ACTUALLY, SHERIFF...

THEY WILL COME TO US!

WHAT? WHY?

WHAT'S GOING ON, ROBIN?

ROBIN? *YOU?*

AS PROMISED, SHERIFF, I HAVE SHOWN YOU ROBIN HOOD.

NOW LIVE UP TO YOUR WORD, AND PAY ME THE EIGHTY MARKS YOU PROMISED.

BEFORE YOU ANSWER, CONSIDER ALL THE ARROWS POINTING AT YOU AND YOUR MEN.

YOU SHOULD BE HAPPY YOU'RE ONLY LOSING MONEY, SHERIFF. MANY OF THE MEN HERE BEAR YOU A SPECIAL GRUDGE.

IF IT WEREN'T FOR YOUR KIND WIFE, WAITING AT HOME, YOU MIGHT SUFFER WORSE.

FOR THE SUPPER SHE PROVIDED AND FOR INTRODUCING ME TO LORD FITZWALTER'S DAUGHTER, I OWE YOUR LADY GREATLY. TELL HER THAT I WILL SEND A PRESENT.

PERHAPS A GENTLE PALFREY* FOR HER TO RIDE. SOMETHING TO REMIND BOTH HER AND YOU OF THE DAY YOU DINED WITH ROBIN HOOD!

*A LADY'S LIGHT HORSE

ROBIN HOOD AND MAID MARIAN

*A*FTER HIS EMBARRASSMENT, THE SHERIFF OF NOTTINGHAM TRIED EVEN HARDER TO CATCH ROBIN OR ANY OF HIS MEN. THE OUTLAWS HAD TO BE MORE CAREFUL THAN EVER. THEY POSTED MORE LOOKOUTS IN THE FOREST AND EVEN CARRIED SWORDS TO HELP PROTECT THEMSELVES.

SO WHEN A PAGE CAME SNEAKING INTO SHERWOOD NOT LONG AFTER, IT WAS NO SURPRISE THAT AN OUTLAW WAS THERE TO BLOCK THE PATH, FEARING SOME SORT OF TRAP.

YOU *MUST* TAKE ME TO ROBIN HOOD! I *HAVE* TO SPEAK WITH HIM.

HOW DO I KNOW YOU'RE NOT THE SHERIFF'S SPY? ANYTHING YOU HAVE TO SAY TO HIM, YOU CAN SAY TO ME.

ARE YOU ALL RIGHT, ROBIN?

I'LL BE FINE, MUCH.

ROBIN? OH, NO! I COULD HAVE KILLED YOU!

MARIAN! WHAT ARE YOU *DOING* HERE?

OH, ROBIN, IT'S ME! MARIAN FITZWALTER!

JUST A SCRATCH, REALLY. MY OWN FAULT FOR BEING TOO CAUTIOUS I SUPPOSE.

NOW WHAT IS IT YOU HAVE TO TELL ME, LAD?

I COULDN'T BELIEVE IT WHEN THE SHERIFF SAID OUR JOLLY POTTER WAS ROBIN HOOD! AND I HAD KISSED YOU!

NEVER MIND! THAT DOESN'T MATTER. WHAT I NEED TO TELL YOU IS THIS—I OVERHEARD MY FATHER TALKING WITH THE SHERIFF.

BUT MY FATHER WARNED HIM THAT THE KING WOULDN'T LIKE HIS SHERIFF, THE MAN CHARGED WITH KEEPING THE PEACE IN NOTTINGHAMSHIRE, COMING TO HIM FOR HELP.

THE SHERIFF WAS TALKING ABOUT GOING TO THE KING! GETTING HIS HELP TO HUNT YOU DOWN. HE WAS SO FURIOUS AFTER YOU SENT HIS WIFE THAT PALFREY!

ROBIN HOOD
AND THE SILVER ARROW

WHEN THE DAY OF THE ARCHERY
CONTEST ARRIVED, THE SHERIFF OF
NOTTINGHAM GAZED ANXIOUSLY AT
THE ARCHERS, TRYING TO SEE IF
ONE OF THEM WAS ROBIN HOOD.

BOTH HIS WIFE AND MAID MARIAN
WERE AFRAID FOR THE BRAVE
OUTLAW, BUT WERE CAREFUL NOT TO
SAY SO. MARIAN'S FATHER, LORD
FITZWALTER, JUST SEEMED
CURIOUS TO SEE IF THE TRICK
WOULD WORK.

WHERE IS
HE? WHERE
IS HE?

TO MAKE HIS TRAP HARDER TO RESIST, THE SHERIFF HAD SENT MESSENGERS ALL ACROSS ENGLAND TO BRING THE BEST ARCHERS IN THE ENTIRE KINGDOM TO THE CONTEST.

HE KNEW THAT ROBIN WOULD WANT TO *PROVE* HE WAS THE BEST ARCHER IN ALL OF ENGLAND.

I TAKE IT YOU DON'T SEE HIM?

THEY'RE TOO FAR AWAY. I'LL GET A CLOSER LOOK WHEN THEY SHOOT.

DO YOUR *REALLY* THINK HE'LL COME?

I'M SURE OF IT. I ONLY PRAY HE'S AS CLEVER AS HE THINKS.

THERE WERE ALMOST FIVE SCORE ARCHERS TO START. EACH SHOT ONE ARROW. TEN WHO SHOT THE BEST STAYED IN THE CONTEST.

THEN THOSE TEN WOULD SHOOT TWO ARROWS EACH, AND THE THREE BEST WOULD STAY ON.

DO YOU KNOW THESE MEN WHO ARE STILL IN THE CONTEST? COULD ONE BE ROBIN HOOD?

I THINK NOT. OF THE TEN REMAINING, THERE ARE FIVE OF MY MEN. THE OTHER FOUR ARE WELL KNOWN FOR THEIR SHOOTING SKILL. THAT LEAVES THE ONE-EYED, BROWN-BEARDED BEGGAR.

BUT WE BOTH KNOW ROBIN HOOD HAS A YELLOW BEARD AND TWO GOOD EYES. WHO WOULD SHOOT ONE-EYED WHO DIDN'T HAVE TO?

OF THE TEN WHO REMAINED, THE THREE WHO SHOT BEST WOULD BE IN THE FINAL MATCH.

SHHHHKK!!

UNBELIEVABLE! HOW IS IT THAT A BEGGAR HAS BECOME SO GOOD WITH A BOW?

THESE ARE DIFFICULT TIMES, MY LORD SHERIFF, AND A MAN MUST PROTECT HIMSELF.

FROM OUTLAWS, YOU MEAN? LIKE ROBIN HOOD? BAH! HE WAS TOO FRIGHTENED TO EVEN COME TO THIS CONTEST!

IF YOU SAY SO, MY LORD SHERIFF. MIGHT I ASK A FAVOUR, IF YOU PLEASE?

WHAT'S THAT?

MARIAN?

I'D BE HAPPY TO.

MIGHT I RECEIVE THE PRIZE FROM THE LOVELY MAIDEN'S HAND? AS A BEGGAR, IT IS THE CLOSEST I WILL COME TO SUCH BEAUTY.

GLOSSARY

ARCHER: a person who uses a bow and arrow

BEGGAR: a person who lives by asking for food or money

BOON: a timely benefit; a blessing

FORESTER: a man hired to guard the forest from outlaws

KNIGHT: a man devoted to the service of a superior, such as a king or lord

LORD: an English nobleman

MAIDEN: an unmarried girl or woman

MARK: an old English unit of currency

MILLER: a person who grinds grain into flour

NOBLEMAN: a man of high rank; an aristocrat

PALFREY: a lady's light horse

POTTER: a person who makes pottery

QUARTERSTAFF: a long staff used for fighting

SCORE: twenty things

SCOUNDREL: a rascal, troublemaker

TRADESMAN: a worker in a skilled trade

YEOMAN: a middle-class English landowner

pencil sketch from page 18

FURTHER READING, WEBSITES, AND FILMS

The Adventures of Robin Hood. DVD. Directed by Michael Curtiz. Hollywood: Warner Bros. Pictures, 1938. This fun and exciting film, starring Errol Flynn as Robin and Olivia De Havilland as Maid Marian, is one of the most popular movies of all time.

The Geste of Robin Hood
http://web.ics.purdue.edu?~ohlgren/gesttrans.html
Visit this website to read a contemporary translation of one of the original ballads of Robin Hood's adventures. The original geste (folk song) was composed in Middle English in the fifteenth century.

Green, Arthur. *The Adventures of Robin Hood.* London: Puffin Classics, 2004. The classic story of social justice and outrageous cunning. Robin Hood is champion of the poor and oppressed by twelfth-century England against the cruel power of Prince John and the brutal Sheriff of Nottingham.

Knight, Stephen. *Robin Hood: A Complete Study of the English Outlaw.* Oxford: Wiley Blackwell Ltd, 1994. Knight's study, based on literary and sociocultural research, provides an analytic account of this figure, the English outlaw who has symbolized resistance to authority around the world for over 500 years.

Pyle, Howard. *The Merry Adventures of Robin Hood.* New York: Signet Classics, 1986. Howard Pyle's illustrated adaptations of the Robin Hood stories are some of the most famous and popular in the world.

Robin Hood: A Beginner's Guide to Robin Hood
http://www.boldoutlaw.com/robbeg/robbeg1.html
This Web page provides a brief overview of the legend of Robin Hood and his many adventures. The page is part of a larger site that features a great deal of helpful information about the Outlaw of Sherwood Forest.

Robin Hood. DVD. Directed by John Irvin. Hollywood: 20th Century Fox, 1991. This action-packed made-for-TV movie stars Patrick Bergin as Robin and Uma Thurman as Maid Marian.

Storrie, Paul D. *William Tell: One Against an Empire.* London: Lerner Books, 2010. He wanted nothing more than to live in peace until a petty tyrant forced him into a cruel choice.

Williams, Marcia. *The Adventures of Robin Hood.* London: Walker Books Ltd, 2007. Told in lively comic-strip style, this book relates eleven colourful action-packed tales about Robin and his merry men. Read how Robin becomes an outlaw.

CREATING *ROBIN HOOD: OUTLAW OF SHERWOOD FOREST*

Author Paul D. Storrie relied heavily on the earliest versions of the Robin Hood stories available: the lyrics to the medieval songs about Robin and his followers. His research also included the excellent books *Robin Hood* by J. C. Holt and *Robin Hood: A Complete Study of the English Outlaw* by Stephen Thomas Knight. Artist Thomas Yeates referred to modern sources of medieval dress as well as to illustrations by great artists of the past, including Howard Pyle, Harold Foster, and N. C. Wyeth. Professor Andrew Scheil of the University of Minnesota lent his time and expertise in reviewing this project.

INDEX

ABOUT THE AUTHOR AND THE ARTIST

PAUL D. STORRIE was born and raised in Detroit, Michigan, and has returned to
live there again and again after living in other cities and states. He has been a
fan of Robin Hood tales his entire life, and his very first published work was
the 1987 comic book series Robyn of Sherwood about the daughter of the
legendary archer. Since then, he has written several comic book stories about
Robin Hood himself. His other works includes *Batman Beyond*, *Justice
League Adventures*, and *Gotham Girls* for DC Comics and contributions to
Captain America: Red, White & Blue and *Mutant X: Dangerous Decisions*
for Marvel. He has also written *Hercules: The Twelve Labors* in the Graphic
Myths and Legends series.

THOMAS YEATES Originally from Sacramento, California, Thomas Yeates began
his art training in high school and continued it at Utah State University and
at Sacramento State. Subsequently, he was a member of the first class at Joe
Kubert's School, a trade program for aspiring comic book artists in New
Jersey. Yeates is strongly influenced in his craft by old-guard illustrators like
Hal Foster, N. C. Wyeth, and Wallace Wood. He has worked as an
illustrator for DC, Marvel, Dark Horse, and many other companies, drawing
Tarzan, *Zorro*, *the Swamp Thing*, *Timespirits*, *Captain America*, and *Conan*,
among others. He has also edited *Al Williamson: Hidden Lands* for Dark
Horse.

First published in the United States of America in 2007